Cancer
Astrology Coloring Book

Color Your Zodiac Sign

DYLANNA
PRESS

The 12 Signs

Sign Symbols

ARIES

TAURUS

GEMINI

CANCER

LEO

VIRGO

LIBRA

SCORPIO

SAGITTARIUS

CAPRICORN

AQUARIUS

PISCES

Cancer

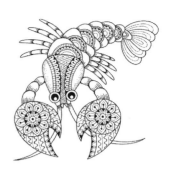

June 21 - July 22

CANCER SIGNS are deeply intuitive and emotional, because of this they can be one of the hardest signs to get close to. They are loyal and have a special ability to empathize with others pain and suffering. This makes them an amazing person to get to know. Ruled by the moon, Cancers are prone to mood swings that come along with the changing lunar phases. They are very private but once they feel comfortable will be trusting and loyal until the end.

Symbol: Crab

Planet: Moon

Element: Water

Color: White

Traits: Loyal, Protective, Intuitive, Caring, Sensitive, Moody, Vindictive

Constellation:

CANCER

CANCER

Cancer

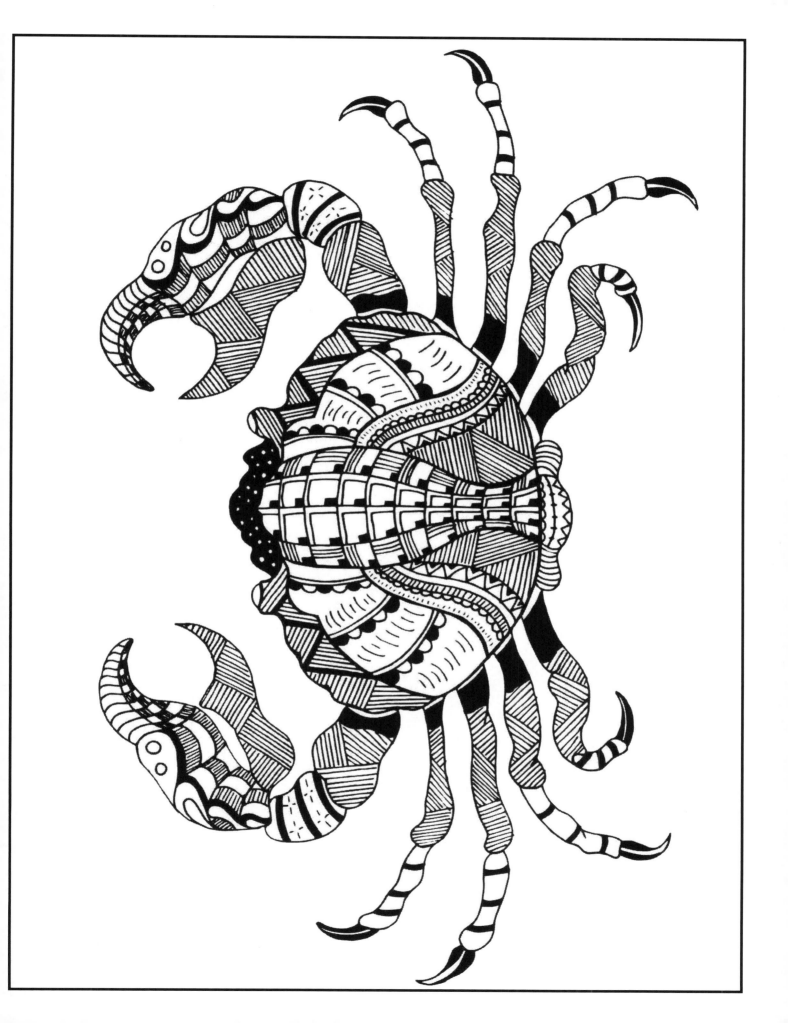

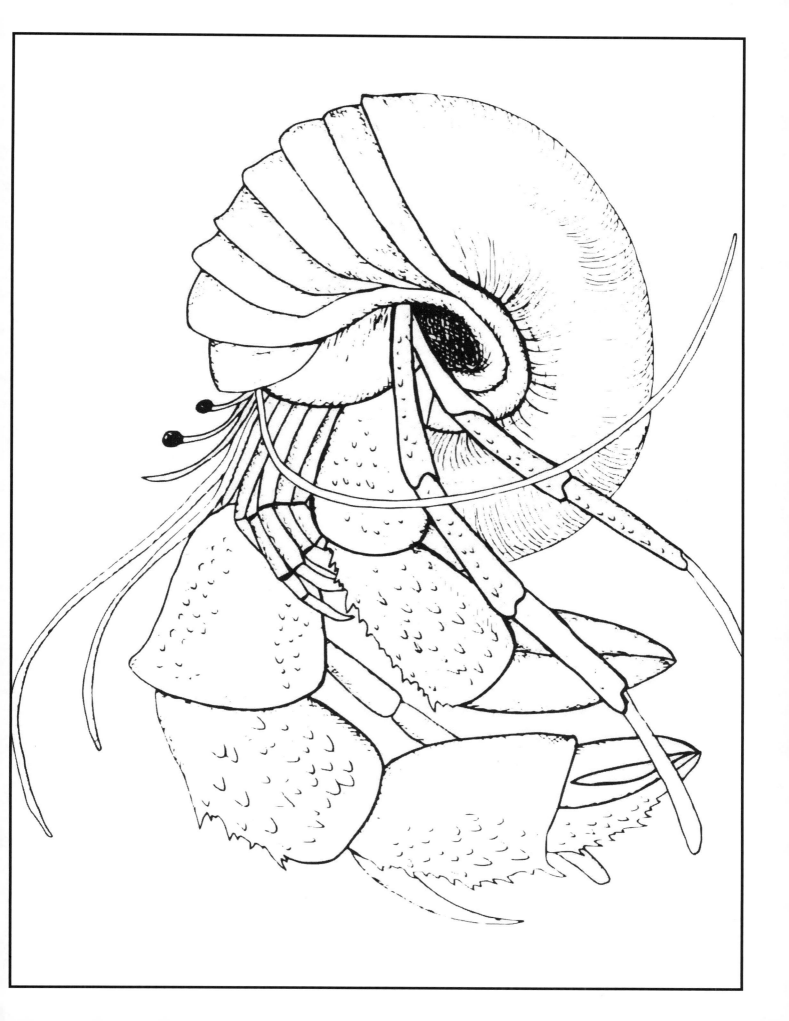

Cancer

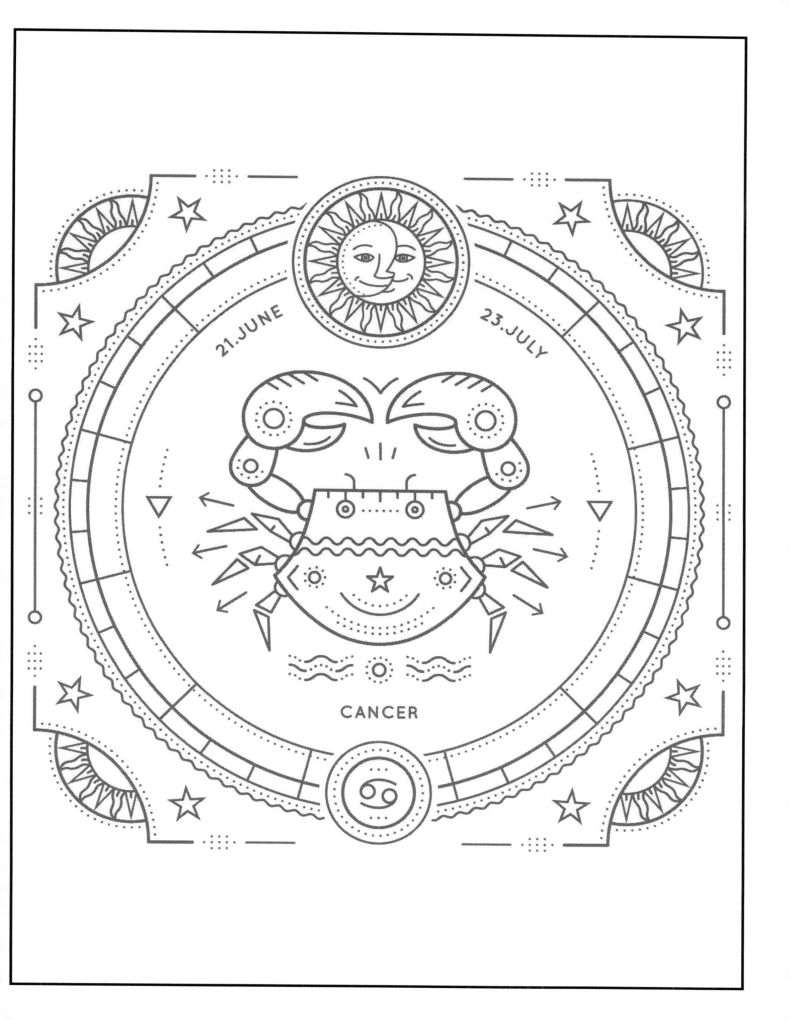

CANCER

Cancer

Made in the USA
Middletown, DE
15 March 2023